Sorting

Draw lines to put each toy into the c

CW00392503

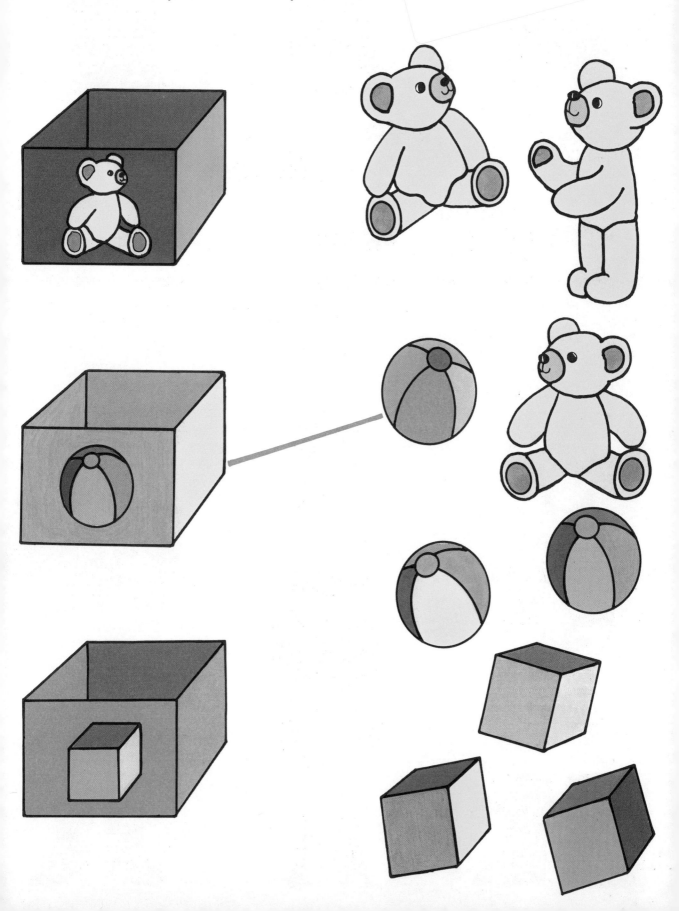

Sorting colours

Draw a line to put the cars in the correct garage.

Sorting sizes

Which boots fit each pirate?

Matching

Draw a line to join those things which are **the same**.

 **one**

Here is **one** aeroplane.

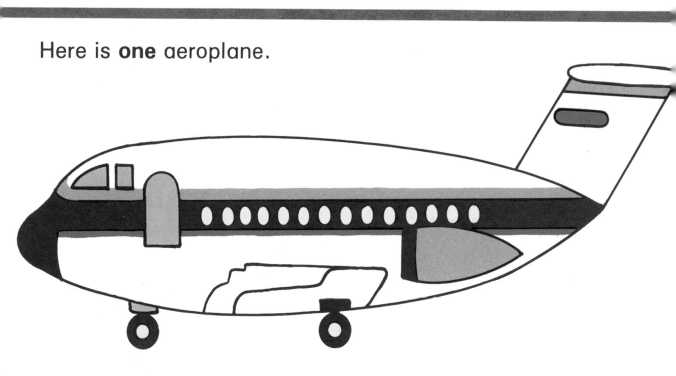

This is the numeral for one
Start at the green spot.
Draw over the dotted line.

Draw some more here.

A ship

Draw **one** ship here.

How many mice?

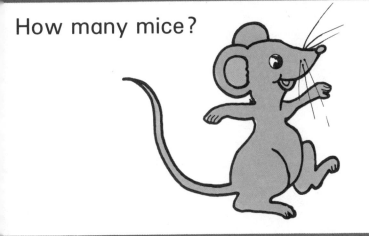

Write the numeral here.

_____

one

l butterfly

Draw **l more** butterfly.

2 two

Here are **two** elephants.

This is the numeral for two
Draw over the dotted line.

2

Draw some more here.

A zebra
Draw **two** zebras.

How many apples?

Write the
numeral
here.

_____

two

2 oranges

Draw **I more** orange.

3 three

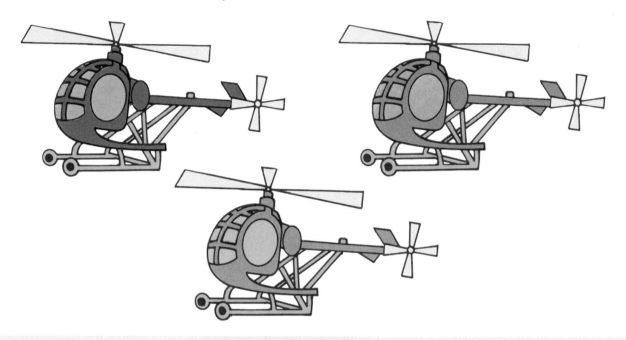

Here are **three** helicopters.

This is the numeral for three **3**
Draw over the dotted line.

Draw some more here.

1 2 3

A kite

Draw **three** kites.

How many spacemen?

Write the
numeral
here.

_____

three

3 rockets

Draw **I more** rocket.

4 four

Here are **four** cats.

This is the numeral for four   4
Draw over the dotted line.

Draw some more here.

1 2 3 4

A mouse
Draw **four** mice.

How many dogs?

Write the
numeral
here.

_____

four

4 rabbits

Draw **1 more** rabbit.

5 five

Here are **five** mugs.

This is the numeral for five
Draw over the dotted line.

5

Draw some more here.

1 2 3 4 5

A bowl

Draw **five** bowls.

How many plates?

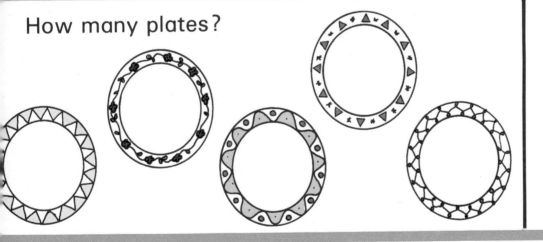

Write the
numeral
here.

_____

five

5 spoons

Draw **I more** spoon.

6 six

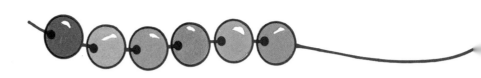

Here are **six** trees.

The numeral for six is
Draw over the dotted line. 6

6 6 6 6 6 6

Draw some more here.

1 2 3 4 5 6

A flower

Draw **six** flowers.

How many birds?

Write the numeral here.

_____

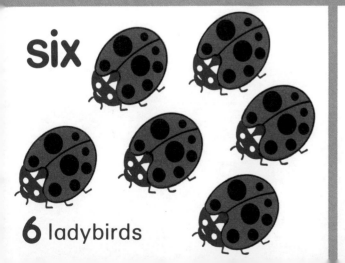

six

6 ladybirds

Draw **I more** ladybird.

7 seven

Here are **seven** sheep.

The numeral for seven is **7**
Draw over the dotted line.

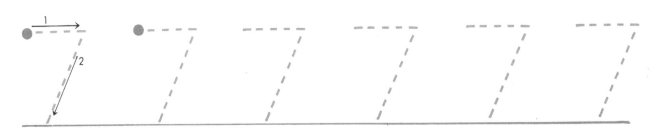

Draw some more here.

1 2 3 4 5 6 7

A hen

Draw **seven** hens.

How many cows?

Write the numeral here.

_____

seven

7 ducks

Draw **I more** duck.

8 eight

Here are **eight** crabs.

The numeral for eight is **8**
Draw over the dotted line.

Draw some more here.

1 2 3 4 5 6 7 8

A fish
Draw **eight** fish.

How many octopuses?

Write the
numeral
here.

_____

eight

8 starfish

Draw **I more** starfish.

9 nine

Here are **nine** frogs.

The numeral for nine is **9**
Draw over the dotted line.

Draw some more here.

1 2 3 4 5 6 7 8 9

A butterfly
Draw **nine** butterflies.

How many snails?

Write the
numeral
here.

_____

nine

9 bees

Draw **I more** bee.

10 ten

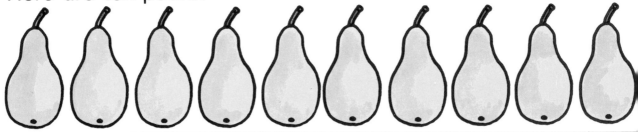

Here are **ten** pears.

A banana

Draw **ten** bananas.

The numeral for ten is **10**
Draw over the dotted line.

Draw some more here.

1 2 3 4 5 6 7 8 9 10

The rocket must go to each planet in the correct order.
Draw a line to show
its journey.

Count the things in the picture and write the numerals in the boxes.
How many

moons? ☐ witches? ☐ cats? ☐ toadstools? ☐

dragons? ☐ owls? ☐ bats? ☐ stars? ☐